SCIENTIFIC PRINCIPLES
AND MORAL CONDUCT

BY

JAMES B. CONANT

President Emeritus
Harvard University

THE TWENTIETH ARTHUR STANLEY
EDDINGTON MEMORIAL LECTURE
DELIVERED AT
PRINCETON UNIVERSITY
15 NOVEMBER 1966

CAMBRIDGE
AT THE UNIVERSITY PRESS
1967

Published by the Syndics of the Cambridge University Press
Bentley House, 200 Euston Road, London, N.W. 1.
American Branch: 32 East 57th Street, New York, N.Y. 10022

Library of Congress Catalogue Card Number: 67-26067

Printed in Great Britain
at the University Printing House, Cambridge
(Brooke Crutchley, University Printer)

THE ARTHUR STANLEY EDDINGTON
MEMORIAL LECTURESHIP

This Lectureship was instituted in 1947 with the intention of providing a fitting memorial to Sir Arthur Eddington, O.M., Plumian Professor of Astronomy in the University of Cambridge from 1913 to 1944.

The lectures are to deal with some aspect of contemporary scientific thought considered in its bearing on the philosophy of religion or on ethics. It is hoped that they will thus help to maintain and further Eddington's concern for relating the scientific, the philosophical and the religious methods of seeking truth and will be a means of developing that insight into the unity underlying these different methods which was his characteristic aim.

Man's rapidly increasing control over natural forces holds out prospects of material achievements that are dazzling ; but unless this increased control of material power can be matched by a great moral and spiritual advance, it threatens the catastrophic breakdown of human civilization. Consequently, the need was never so urgent as now for a synthesis of the kind of understanding to be gained through various ways—scientific, philosophical and religious—of seeking truth.

The Lectureship is managed by a Board of four Trustees appointed by The Royal Society, Trinity College, Cambridge, and the Society of Friends.

W.H. THORPE, *Chairman of the Trustees*
JESUS COLLEGE, CAMBRIDGE
W.B. HARLAND, *Secretary to the Trustees*
GONVILLE AND CAIUS COLLEGE, CAMBRIDGE

LECTURES ON THIS FOUNDATION

1. Reflections on the Philosophy of Sir Arthur Eddington, by A. D. RITCHIE
2. Sir Arthur Eddington: Man of Science and Mystic, by L. P. JACKS
3. The Unity of Knowledge, by GEORGE B. JEFFERY, F.R.S.
4. Creative Aspects of Natural Law, by R. A. FISHER, F.R.S.
5. Eddington's Principle in the Philosophy of Science, by Sir EDMUND WHITTAKER, F.R.S.
6. Time and Universe for the Scientific Conscience, by MARTIN JOHNSON
7. Some Aspects of the Conflict between Science and Religion, by H. H. PRICE
8. The Sources of Eddington's Philosophy, by HERBERT DINGLE
9. An Empiricist's View of the Nature of Religious Belief, by R. B. BRAITHWAITE
10. Thought, Life and Time, as reflected in Science and Poetry, by H. G. WOOD
11. Science and the Idea of God, by C. A. COULSON, F.R.S.
12. Science, Philosophy and Religion, by Sir RUSSELL BRAIN, Bt.
13. Beyond Nihilism, by MICHAEL POLANYI, F.R.S.
14. Biology, Psychology and Belief, by W. H. THORPE, F.R.S.
15. The Vision of Nature, by Sir CYRIL N. HINSHELWOOD, O.M., D.Sc., P.P.R.S.
16. On Having a Mind, by WILLIAM KNEALE, F.B.A.
17. Mind and Consciousness in Experimental Psychology, by R. H. THOULESS
18. I Believe..., by KATHLEEN LONSDALE, D.B.E., F.R.S.
19. The Brain and the Unity of Conscious Experience, by Sir JOHN ECCLES, F.R.S.
20. Scientific Principles and Moral Conduct, by JAMES B. CONANT

4

Scientific principles and moral conduct

THE Arthur Stanley Eddington Memorial Lectureship was established in 1947. I have the honour to be the twentieth lecturer and the first to give the lecture in the United States. In expressing my appreciation of the distinction, I should like to record my acute awareness of the challenge. The trustees have laid it down that 'the lectures are to deal with some aspect of contemporary scientific thought considered in its bearing on the philosophy of religion or on ethics. It is hoped that they will thus help to maintain and further Eddington's concern for relating the scientific, the philosophical and religious methods of seeking truth and will be a means of developing that insight into the unity underlying these different methods which was his characteristic aim. 'The need was never so urgent for a synthesis of the kind of understanding to be gained through various ways—scientific, philosophical and religious—of seeking truth.'

The words which I have just quoted were written about twenty years ago. Science today is far in advance of what it was when the Eddington Memorial Lectureship was founded. Yet any attempt to relate scientific thought to what the trustees have called 'the philosophical and religious ways of seeking truth' is still a perilous undertaking. Indeed I am inclined to think that in the

5

United States, at least, the spectacular advances in physical and biological science and in engineering have tended to make the task more difficult than ever before. The fact that scientists in this century have been so successful in advancing science has led many to believe that there must be some special method which has guided their endeavours. If one assumes there is such a thing as *the* scientific method, one can then argue that the method must be applicable to all human endeavours. If this be so, a widespread knowledge of the method, and a determination to apply it, might well lead to the disappearance of those problems which concern moral philosophers and at times theologians. From this it follows that there is no need to relate three ways of seeking truth; there is only one way—the scientific. So the argument goes. It is not new. I am inclined to think, however, that it is more widely accepted than ever before.

To my mind the line of reasoning I have just presented is completely false. It rests on a mis-reading of the history of science. Science did not start to prosper because a new method was formulated and applied. The growth of modern science is a complex phenomenon. Any account of it must show the stumbling way in which the pioneers in each area had to struggle through a jungle of false observations and wild speculations. Even today in the most sophisticated branches of natural science, advances are not made by the application of a single method. There are many techniques, many ways of stating problems, many methods of analysis. Yet, belief in a mistaken notion about experimental science is widespread. Many elementary texts in the physical and biological sciences perpetuate it. One author, for example, states that there is a series of eight steps in the scientific method beginning with the 'recognition of an indeterminate situation' and ending with an 'assertion which appears to be warranted' and which is unified with the body of knowledge already established. Such an account of the way scientists operate makes no distinction between the solution of a trivial problem and the advances which mark a breakthrough into new knowledge—a minor or major scientific revolution. To be sure, the way an experimental scientist proceeds to seek a solution to a given problem is not dissimilar to the way the same person as a householder endeavours to find what is wrong when all the lights suddenly go out. The problem is stated, an hypothesis put forward, tests of the hypothesis are made which either confirm or refute it; for example, the hypothesis might be that a short in an old lamp has caused the blowing of a fuse. But even a dressed-up version of such thoughts and actions does not constitute a new method developed a few centuries ago.

The various formulations of the scientific method I have read are hardly more than a description of the trial-and-error procedures which have been employed in the practical arts ever since our distant ancestors became tool makers. What was new about the time of Galileo was the slow merging of the inventive tinkering of artisans with the abstract reasoning of mathematicians. Years ago I suggested that science emerged from the other activities of man when a few people began to see the significance of the new concepts arising from experiment and observation.[1] These new concepts in turn led to further experiments and observations. Scientific knowledge grew with increasing rapidity as more and more men of genius turned to experimentation. The fruitful concepts became interwoven into a texture which we recognize as modern science. The test of a new idea was not only its success in correlating the then-known facts but its success or failure in stimulating further experimentation or observation which was fruitful. It was the dynamic quality of science viewed as the continuous activity of an increasing number of men which seemed to me to be close to the heart of the best definition. And I added that the truth of my definition could only be demonstrated by the historical approach or else learned by direct professional experience.[2]

I am of the same opinion today. This fact places me in an embarrassing position as an Eddington Lecturer, I must admit. In order to meet the challenge of relating three ways of seeking truth, I have to substitute for the words 'scientific method' some such phrase as 'the way science has advanced'. Such a change is necessary because the success of natural scientists, which is the point of reference, is not due primarily to their methods but to the aim of their efforts. And curiously enough the aim is determined every few years by what has been the outcome of the experiments and observations of the preceding years. I appeal to the record of experimental science to justify this statement. An investigator may be likened to a hunter in desperate search for food. He is prepared to shoot whatever appears. He and his friends will label the trip successful even if he brings back game he never knew was to be found in that locality. Of course, one can use such general phrases as 'science aims to disclose the nature of the universe' or 'science seeks the truth', but to discover what such words mean one must escape from generalities and examine specific situations.

I am well aware that many practising scientists do not agree with what may be regarded as my sceptical approach. On the other hand, I could marshal quotations from the writings of both ex-perimentalists and philosophers to support my position.[3] To sum it up in a few words, I find my-self in agreement with the view expressed in 1907 by J. J. Thomson who wrote, 'From the point of view of the physicist, a theory of matter is a policy rather than a creed; its object is to connect or co-ordinate apparently diverse phenomena, and above all to suggest, stimulate and direct experiment.'[4]

Scientific knowledge has grown because of the

activity of scientists. However one defines science, such a statement stands. Therefore, even the believers in the scientific method of seeking truth may be willing to agree that a study of the way a scientist proceeds may be of interest. Further, that a comparison of the principles which guide his conduct as an investigator are worthy of examination in order to see how they differ, if at all, from the principles which guide the same man outside the laboratory. At any rate, such is the task I set before me. Those of you who are familiar with the writings of moral philosophers will have read many discussions of guides to conduct—the word conduct being a synonym for voluntary activity.[5] Such activity involves making choices—that is, coming to a decision, which in turn means adopting a criterion for passing judgment on the decision.

Ethics may be defined as the study of conduct including, of course, the criteria to which I have just referred. The field of ethics is nowadays divided into normative ethics and meta-ethics. The statements in the former contain such words as 'good' and 'bad', 'right' and 'wrong'. Meta-ethics, on the other hand, is concerned only with questions about the meaning, nature or function of normative judgments and about the methods by which they may be justified. Questions in meta-ethics rather than the content of normative systems now seem to dominate ethical discussions. As Professor W. K. Frankena has pointed out, many laymen are disturbed by this relative neglect of normative ethics.[6] But the explanation to his mind is as follows:

The chief intellectual problem of any age in which the foundations have been shaken is bound to be the question whether there are any objective or rational grounds on which we can rest our basic moral principles and value judgments, and, if so, what they are. Now, in other periods this question was expressed by asking whether such principles and judgments rest on *reason* (not limited to science in our sense) or on something else—authority, faith, revelation, sentiment or tradition. But today, when for many people reason has come to be identified with science (except for the analytical truths of logic and mathematics), the problem centres about the question whether normative ethics can be wholly based on science or not.

Emphasizing the word 'wholly', he goes on to say that:

Anyone can admit that given a basic principle or goal, science can tell us what to do in order to bring about the required state of affairs . . . But this would still be saying only that we should enlighten the application of our moral principles or the realization of our moral goals as much as possible by science. The question, however, is whether science can somehow establish those very goals or principles. That is, the main question of ethical theory has been whether or not normative ethics can be put on a scientific basis—or, if you will, whether normative ethics is a science or a humanity.

The question Professor Frankena raises is very close to one which can be stated in terms of the applicability of the methods of science to problems of moral conduct. I have already indicated that I do not believe there is such a thing as *the* scientific method. Therefore, if normative ethics is to be based on science, it cannot, in my opinion, rest on the use of a single method. But can it be based on an analogy with the way science has advanced? Before giving a clear-cut answer to the question, I should like to probe deeper into the nature of scientific knowledge.

To do so let me extend my original definition of science. I shall be bold enough to wrap the mantle of an eminent American logician around me. I present a quotation or two from Professor W. V. Quine's book *From a Logical Point of View*. Under the heading 'Empiricism Without Dogmas'[7] he writes as follows:

The totality of our so-called knowledge or beliefs, from the most casual matters of geography and history to the profoundest laws of atomic physics or even of pure mathematics and logic, is a man-made fabric which impinges on experience only along the edges. Or, to change the figure, total science is like a field of force whose boundary conditions are experience. A conflict with experience at the periphery occasions readjustments in the interior of the field.

Two paragraphs later he explains his metaphor in the following way.

Certain statements, though *about* physical objects and not sense experience, seem peculiarly germane to sense experience—and in a selective way: some statements to some experiences, others to others. Such statements especially germane to particular experiences I picture as near the periphery. But in this relation of 'germaneness' I envisage nothing more than a loose association reflecting the relative likelihood, in practice, of our choosing one statement rather than another for revision in the event of recalcitrant experience.

It is one of the essential elements in the point of view Professor Quine presents that 'our statements about the external world face the tribunal of sense experience not individually but only as a corporate body.'[8] There are a number of cases in the history of science which could be quoted to show how a readjustment of one part of the conceptual scheme has resulted from new developments in a distant area. Take the doctrine of the conservation of weight in a chemical reaction. This postulate was one of the pillars of the new chemistry expounded by Lavoisier in the fourth quarter of the eighteenth century. It remained unquestioned through the nineteenth. If some sixty years ago someone had prophesied that within a lifetime this generalization would be modified, few would have credited the prediction. Thinking back to the elaborate quantitative experiments which had been performed to test the doctrine experimentally, some chemist might have admitted the possibility that even more refined techniques might show that the generalization was not quite accurate. But if the prophet had foretold that the changes which were accepted were beyond the limits of detection by the experimental means available to a chemist, I feel sure that no one would have believed him. And if he had gone on to say that the necessity for the adjustment was the result of a reformulation of basic ideas of physics in which the speed of light would enter the calculations, he probably would have been declared quite mad.

Concepts and conceptual schemes arising from experiment and observation are extensions of those postulates by which men for ages have defined a large part of the so-called external world. Belief in the reality of rocks and trees, water and ice, and the certainty of predictions about the manipulation of physical objects made possible the beginnings of civilization in far distant prehistoric times. For example, one could make a long list of common-sense assumptions that were made by those embryonic metallurgists who learned to win metals from the ores. The modern scientist's belief in the reality of the new postulates of the last few hundred years has enabled him to carry on manipulations literally undreamed of by scientific workers even a century ago. Yet as I see the picture, the difference between the very ancient posits and those of this century is one of degree and not of kind. But once again I bulwark my arguments by quoting from Professor Quine.

As an empiricist I continue to think of the conceptual scheme of science as a tool, ultimately, for predicting future experience in the light of past experience. Physical objects are conceptually imported into the situation as convenient intermediaries—not by definition in terms of experience, but simply as irreducible posits comparable, epistemologically, to the gods of Homer. For my part I do, *qua* lay physicist, believe in physical objects and not in Homer's gods; and I consider it a scientific error to believe otherwise. But in point of epistemological footing the physical objects and the gods differ only in degree and not in kind. Both sorts of entities enter our conception only as cultural posits. The myth of physical objects is epistemologically superior to most in that it has proved more efficacious than other myths as a device for working a manageable structure into the flux of experience.—...Science is a continuation of common sense, and it continues the common-sense expedient of swelling ontology to simplify theory.[9]

I venture to add a footnote to this quotation. Modern science has not only added such posits as atoms, electrons and neutrons but has eliminated some others which were at first useful. I need mention only the caloric fluid and the luminiferous ether. The process of elimination invokes the principles of economy and simplicity. In the course of the development of experimental science, it became accepted practice that in the construction of a theory as few posits as possible would be introduced. That is why, I take it, most of us would agree with Quine in rejecting a belief in Homer's gods. They would constitute unnecessary postulates. To be sure they could be incorporated in the present fabric provided other postulates were also added. These additions would have to be so formulated that there would be no interaction of the Homeric entities with the rest of the conceptual scheme of common sense and science. The net effect would be a multiplication of posits to no avail. A similar procedure might be used if one wanted to maintain the reality of the demons and gnomes which Agricola reported as either attacking or pretending to help the miners in the sixteenth century mines. One could accept them as part of history. Agricola was a reporter whose accuracy on other matters has not been challenged. He was not prone to the speculations of his contemporaries, the alchemists. Logically the existence of the gnomes would be on a par with that of any animal about whom we only have reports. Yet it would seem necessary to add a postulate that gnomes, if they existed, have long since disappeared. A further set of postulates would be necessary to fit these new posits into the fabric of belief which we now accept. I introduce these absurdities only to emphasize that if one disregards the principle of economy, all sorts of adjustments in a conceptual scheme are possible without violating logic.

I am discussing the way science advances. In particular I am examining the principles which determine what an experimentalist does in the course of his investigations. Before we proceed further, however, we would do well to raise a fundamental question: Why should science be advanced? Though there are many arguments today about how the advance of science should be financed, we rarely hear anyone suggest that the entire enterprise be abandoned. We assume that the controlled curiosity which developed in a few nations a few centuries ago is an activity to be honoured. It was not always so. Indeed, it is not uniformly true at the present time among even literate circles the world over. What was new was the emergence of a type of activity which slowly became highly regarded by people of influence and power. We take our favourable attitude toward science for granted but would do well to remember that there are other points of view. In this connection the famous footnote in William James's textbook of psychology may serve as a reminder.[10] James quotes from a reply of a Turkish official in the nineteenth century to an English traveller's request for statistical information.

The thing you ask of me is both difficult and useless...
As to the previous history of this city, God only knows the amount of dirt and confusion that the infidels may have eaten before the coming of the sword of Islam. It were unprofitable for us to inquire into it... Listen, O my son! There is no wisdom equal unto the belief in God! He created the world, and shall we liken ourselves unto Him in seeking to penetrate into the mysteries of His creation?

Whatever the degree of sympathy and understanding one may have for the outlook expressed by the devoted adherent to the Islamic faith, I think all would agree that neither he nor those who think with him would be likely to be effective in the advance of science. Science for the last few generations has been advanced by people who were dedicated to the task. They were and are agreed that it is important that scientific knowledge should be extended. They are also agreed that as scientists they are members of an informal international fellowship to which they owe an allegiance.

As ethical principles there is nothing unique about these two articles of faith. Either one could be made a major premise in a practical syllogism of the type which writers on ethics rejoice in examining. A scientist, for example, arguing with himself or with his wife, might start with the formulation of a major premise: the advance of science is important; and add the minor premise that he would advance science if he continued his experiment for the next two weeks. The conclusion follows that he ought to stay at work and not yield to the temptation to take a two weeks' vacation cruise. To be sure, similar lines of argumentation can be written out for any calling. The historic examples often quoted are the clergy and the military. What is significant for understanding the nature of the advance of science is the fact that only in the last few centuries and in certain subcultures of our western culture would the major premise in the scientist's argument have been considered valid. And I must add that even today it is by no means easy to answer the rare sceptic who stubbornly raises the question: Leaving applied science aside, why should science be advanced?

The relatively recent rapid extension of scientific knowledge is thus connected with the wide acceptance of two ethical principles which would not have been recognized a few centuries ago. Closely related is the fact that in the last hundred years or so, those engaged in scientific studies have become more and more in agreement in the acceptance of what is commonly called the solid basis of knowledge. To those who regard science as a process of discovering the structure of the universe, the high degree of unanimity of opinion of which I speak appears as a consequence of science's being concerned solely with empirical fact. For those who regard science in the terms I have been using, the unanimity is a consequence of the elaboration of a texture of conceptual schemes which provide a basis for further experimentation. Whichever point of view you choose, it is of the utmost importance to recognize that there is widespread agreement as to the principles of science. At the beginning of the development of modern science, this was far from being the case. I say widespread agreement, yet, of course, not complete agreement. If there were no differences of opinion, there would hardly be any room for further investigation. A scientist accepts the current conceptual scheme in its totality but questions certain deductions related to one area which he would say was under investigation. I am referring to the vast number of research undertakings the results of which added together constitute the annual advance of science. Major scientific revolutions are another story, as Professor T. S. Kuhn has so clearly pointed out.[11]

To return to my hypothetical investigator who stayed in his laboratory, he is in the process of making decisions as his work progresses. Each step might be analysed as a series of choices. Clearly each choice is largely determined by the acceptance of many, many principles of science. Indeed it is hardly necessary to argue that what is commonly called the present status of scientific knowledge functions as an essential component in the argument in which he justifies to himself his choices. Also it is unnecessary to demonstrate that the knowledge in question is different today at least in some respects from what was fifty or sixty years ago. New concepts have been accepted in almost every area. To the extent the current conceptual scheme (to use the words I favour) determines the choice of an experimenter, one may say the principles which guide his actions are not constant. They have changed within the memory of men now living. All that one can do is to bet on how long it will be before drastic changes will occur in one part or another of the man-made fabric.

I have given you my interpretation of the body of principles of the natural sciences and considered how the acceptance of these principles determines the conduct of a scientist in his laboratory. I now turn to the consideration of the same man's conduct when he steps outside. What principles guide his choices and decisions? In other words, I wish to examine the basis for his moral conduct. It goes without saying that I shall not find an answer applicable to all people. Many direct their actions along lines determined by their religious beliefs. Others may accept one or another of the purely naturalistic moral philosophies which have been promulgated from time to time. Still others would be hard pressed to give reasons for the norms of conduct which they nevertheless accept. To the extent that one can fix the content of current normative ethical systems, the religious stand at one extreme, the naturalistic at the other. The arguments of the supporters of one or another of the naturalistic systems are particularly germane to my inquiry because the words 'science' and 'empirical evidence' occur so often in their writings. If it is at all possible to find a normative system that can in any sense be considered as based on science, it should be by following the thinking of these philosophers. But first of all I must examine more closely the nature of the experiences which are basic to *my* definition of science and the ontology

I have taken from Professor Quine. Let me quote one more sentence from his book: 'Our acceptance of an ontology is, I think, similar in principle to our acceptance of a scientific theory, say a system of physics: we adopt, at least in so far as we are reasonable, the simplest conceptual scheme into which the disordered fragments of raw experience can be fitted and arranged.'[12] This sentence sums up what I said earlier about the way I think scientific knowledge should be regarded. I have no idea, however, as to what limitations, if any, Quine had in mind when he wrote the words 'the disordered fragments of raw experience'. As far as I am concerned, however, in discussing both the common-sense world and science, I have had in mind only those experiences which occur in connection with the manipulation of objects, and I underline the word manipulation. The objects to which I have been referring are those of inanimate and animate nature with one important exception. I have not referred to the experiences of primitive man or his modern descendants when confronted with another member of the species *homo sapiens*.

Without explicitly saying so, I have assumed that the conceptual scheme of the external world has been extended by the labours of astronomers, physicists, chemists, geologists, and biologists with enormous assistance from the mathematician. Certainly the great prestige of modern science can be credited to the successful outcome of the experiments and observations of the scientists I have named. There can be no question of that. According to my analysis, it all started with the chipping of flints to make the first stone axes and their use in manipulating other flints and eventually bits of wood. I have said nothing as yet, however, about the use of the axe to threaten or kill a neighbour; I have not touched on the beginnings of social life. I have made no reference to the evolution of those ideas about man and society which were the forerunners of the conceptual schemes by which, early in recorded history, such activities as warfare, politics and trade were analysed. In short the experiences basic to my definition of science by no means encompassed all types of experiences.

Before considering a broadening of the base, let me point out that the conceptual schemes early man created may well have involved little or no distinction between inanimate objects, animals, gods and men. The high degree of animism in some primitive religions is evidence pointing in this direction. The Homeric entities to which I have earlier referred were postulated as being in constant interaction with rocks and trees, storms and animals, as well as men. In organizing his experiences arising from the manipulation of physical objects, plants and animals, modern man in our western culture slowly developed the idea that the posits of supernatural entities were a handicap to his effort. As has been often pointed out, science could not have developed among people who accepted a multiplicity of gods. Philosophic speculations and

23

monotheistic theologies were necessary precursors to the weaving of the fabric of modern science. Yet as I have depicted the growth of the conceptual scheme, the limitations on the experiences involved are such as to ignore those many experiences which involve in important ways other human beings. To handle the experiences arising from encounters between persons, the commonsense external world appears to need extension in some other way than by the highly successful process I have called 'advancing science'.

Professor Morton White has raised much the same issue. He refers to the view (originally put forward by Pierre Duhem) that in testing a scientific prediction one puts to the test a whole body of beliefs. He writes:

But this view, most recently advocated by Quine, is usually limited to the case where (1) a system of scientific discourse is related to (2) sensory experience. When we study the logic of ethical argument, however, we must broaden our linguistic structure so that it includes ethical statements, and broaden the other element in the situation beyond sensory experience to include moral feelings of approval, revulsion, loathing, etc., towards actions.[13]

Since I am engaged in an examination of the guides to conduct of my scientist outside his laboratory, I too must include all manner of experiences. I must broaden the base of any conceptual scheme to which I venture to relate moral principles. I do not propose, however, to remove the limitations I have placed on the experiences basic to the definition of science I have been using. Rather I am going to introduce two additional categories of experience and show their relation to the conceptual scheme about which I have spoken at so great a length. But I must warn you that what I am suggesting finds no support as far as I am aware from the philosophers from whom I have been quoting. From here on, I am strictly on my own.

The two additional categories of experience I am adding are as follows: one includes all the experiences that arise when a person is confronted by one or more members of the human race in any significant way, except for religious experiences (using the phrase as does William James in his famous book).[14] Religious experiences I place in a separate category. These two categories, together with the one in which science is an extension of the common-sense physical world, make up the totality of human experience. In other words, I have divided all experiences into three segments. Let me call these segments the realm of nature, the realm of human nature, the realm of religious experiences. The conceptual schemes in each of these segments are man-made fabrics, and each must stand the test of consistency and simplicity. In each segment or category, except the first, there is more than one man-made fabric; indeed, what distinguishes the first category from the other two is that, today, there is such a unanimity of opinion as regards the postulates constituting the elements of the fabric. In contrast, in the third segment (the one embracing religious experiences) there is a vast number of systems from which an individual must choose even within the Judaic-Christian tradition. And let me remark at this point that while I am engaged in an attempt to find a rational way of ordering experiences of all sorts, I am well aware that in the third realm the choice is often made not on the grounds of logic but because of emotional experiences in childhood. The justification of the choice, however, may be and usually is stated in terms of a conceptual scheme with many posits.

What about a unifying world hypothesis or theory which can bring together the essential elements in each of the three segments? To me, any such effort is a presumptuous undertaking. As I wrote some fifteen years ago, 'Whether the unifying principle be a dualism of matter and spirit, mechanism, formism, or some form of idealism, the whole attempt seems to me to be in the wrong direction. My preference would be for more adequate exploration of special limited areas of experience.'[15] Yet in repeating this statement I wish to dissociate myself from any obscurantist interpretation of my presentation. I am far from wishing to leave the explorer of each of the two other segments of experience to postulate whatever he likes without regard to the postulates of science and common sense. Confrontation of a specific

26

deduction from the conceptual scheme of one
category with a relevant deduction from another
is my suggested substitute for attempts to formu-
late a world hypothesis. Every thoughtful person
must function at times as a lay physicist (as Quine
has used the phrase), at almost all times as a moralist, and many people function at times as lay
theologians. I should consider it a mark of an
obscurantist to be unwilling to confront deductions from one's universe as a lay physicist with
deductions from one's ideas as a moralist or lay
theologian. For example, if to accommodate my
own or accepted reports of religious experiences,
I must postulate miracles, then I am under obliga-
tion, to the extent that I am a man of reason, to
confront this conclusion with a deduction from
the conceptual scheme I accept as a lay physicist.
Similar considerations might apply to the postula-
tion of the continuation of personality after death.
Deductions from the belief in an immortal soul,
however, can at present hardly be confronted
with specific deductions from the current account
of the evolution of the human species. There are
far too many blanks in our beliefs as lay (or professional) biologists about the time, place and manner of the appearance of the first talking animals.
But at some future time a large number of new
posits may have been added to our biology to
accommodate new findings. The nature of man
as seen by the biologist may then be detailed in
terms of his evolution. When that time comes, it

would make sense to ask the following question: Does the belief in immortality conflict with the belief in the principles of biology? Until that day arrives, however, it would appear to me to be unprofitable to debate an issue which we are unable to define clearly because of the paucity of our knowledge of biology.

The considerations I have just set forth point to the necessity of making quite clear the difference between a well-buttressed part of the total conceptual scheme and purely speculative ideas. To be sure, speculative ideas have at times generated concepts which have later been turned into concepts arising from experiment. The history of atomism comes to mind. However, until a speculative idea has been widely accepted and become incorporated in the fabric of science, it is not in the status of the posits to which I have directed your attention. It seems to me some of the popular expositions of science fail to make clear the distinction I have in mind. For example, as a result of experiments and observations in the last forty or fifty years, the postulates involved in the theory of evolution appear as firmly embedded as the postulates of chemical elements. The experiments which demonstrate the role of RNA and DNA in genetics have a peculiar fascination for a former investigator in the field of organic chemistry, I must admit. But quite apart from my personal predilections, it appears that advances in molecular biology as well as those in other areas have made unlikely any drastic changes in the basic theory of evolution. The present ideas about the origin of life on the other hand seem to be in an entirely different situation. They are not as yet part of a scheme which has arisen from experiment and observation. The so-called 'simulation experiments' may be taken as evidence available from the laboratory to support one speculation or another. What is lacking are experiments necessary to support firmly the first stages of the growth of a theory. Whether I am correct or not in my appraisal of the current hypotheses about the origin of life is a small matter. The issue of the place of speculative ideas about the origin and composition of the universe, however, is of considerable importance.

If one regards the whole enterprise of advancing science as a developing picture of reality, then speculation may seem to be on a par with experimentation. On the other hand, if one speaks of a consistent body of scientific beliefs as a policy, not a creed, then whether a given idea has as yet been incorporated in the man-made fabric is significant. The proposal I have made of confrontations of specific deductions from one category of experience with specific deductions from the conceptual scheme of science becomes almost impossible once purely speculative ideas are given the same status as the accepted posits of scientific discourse.

It is time that I returned to my quest for a normative system that can be considered as based on science. Where would such a system be located among the three segments of total experience? Clearly, a naturalistic normative scheme is not to be found in the realm of religious experience. It is equally clear that it can be located in the realm of human nature. What about decisions made solely with reference to the concepts in the realm of nature, the common-sense world extended by natural science? At first sight one might be ready to say that ethical or moral choices could be located in either the realm of nature or the realm of human nature. Philosophers of different schools of thought are fond of illustrating their arguments by referring to simple choices one makes between material objects, for example buying one make of car instead of another. Without hesitation they label all reasoned choices as ethical or moral, however trivial they may be. For it can be argued (and is argued) that it is impossible to draw a line between a trivial and a significant decision. The point at issue is crucial for the discussion in which I am involved. If the principles are ethical or moral which lead me in everyday life to make a choice that involves only myself and inanimate objects, then the scientific principles which guide a scientist in his work as a scientist can be said to be ethical or moral. You will recall that every step in the scientist's experimentation is determined by his acceptance of the conceptual scheme of the realm of nature. He chooses between one reagent or another, between one wiring diagram or another.

And since the outcome of the experiment and hence perhaps the advance of science may turn on the decision, what is at issue is no trivial matter. A naturalistic moral philosopher might well say here is a case where the criteria for judging what is right or wrong are to be found without introducing any extraneous premise; the criteria are generated by the application of the scientific principles themselves; a system of normative ethics is at hand in which science establishes the goals or principles. (The premise that science ought to be advanced, which we have already noted, may conveniently be ignored.)

The train of reasoning I have been giving is intriguing. Yet is it anything more than the old claim that the so-called scientific method has wide applicability? Or at least is it more than a claim that the conduct of a research man as an investigator is guided by the same kind of principles as a person trying to act morally? The analogy is tempting, but I am convinced quite false. Normative systems must be located in the realm of human nature if not in the realm of religious experiences. (Surely most, if not all, moral problems involve other people.) But the realm of human nature unlike the realm of nature is *not* characterized by one conceptual scheme. Quite the contrary. The writings of learned men in different cultures have developed many different concepts to order the experiences associated with personal encounters. There is no equivalent to the extension of the common-sense world by experiment and observation. Therefore, the principles which guide the conduct of a scientist in his work as a scientist are located in one realm, the experiences basic to any normative scheme in another. The two sets of principles are different in kind and not analogous. If I am right, the point is not without its significance not only for ethical theory but for my definition of science.

Another way of seeing the fallacy of considering the conduct of the scientist in his laboratory as a model for moral conduct is to note what happens if we replace the research man striving to advance science with an applied scientist. At once we see additional premises must be introduced, other decisions must precede such decisions as choosing the right reagent. One need only to mention the questions raised by some scientists as to the morality of developing poison gases in the First World War, or the atomic bomb in the Second World War. The advance of the medical sciences might be considered as a case where applied research is proceeding, just as pure research is often conceived as advancing, without any extraneous assumptions. Yet a moment's consideration reminds us that advances in the medical sciences, as distinct from advances in the physical and biological sciences, depend on success in curing disease, preventing death, alleviating suffering. All of which we may be certain are desirable ends, but they are not generated by the advance of science. Like the Hippocratic oath for the physician, they

32

are limitations accepted by the scientist when he works on the production of a new drug and rejected if he synthesizes a new poison gas.

To my mind, there is no escape from the conclusion that ethics cannot be based on science. To be sure, I am equating the word science with modern natural science. But do any of the proponents of the scientific method have in mind ancient science or the modern social sciences as examples of the successful solving of problems? I doubt it. The advances in the natural sciences in the last two hundred years are what people have in mind who worship science. And it is just these advances, I contend, which justify my definition of science. If you accept it and Professor Quine's ontology, then the activity of a natural scientist, as scientist, is different in kind from the other activities of modern man. The fundamental reason, the reader will note, is because according to my analysis only one type of raw experience has been considered by those who, over the last few centuries, have attempted to construct a conceptual scheme which is an extension of common sense.

The result of the limitation of the kind of experiences being ordered is an extraordinary agreement as to the postulates which are a necessary part of the conceptual scheme of natural science. They are closely related to the posits which are basic to our belief in a common-sense physical world. They arise from a consideration of the raw experiences associated with the manipulation of an object, whether it be a stone by means of a man's foot or a measuring instrument by means of his hands.

It will be noted that one result of my trichotomy is to place the natural sciences on a distinctly different epistemological footing from the social sciences. To me astronomy, for example, is a science in quite a different sense of the word than is political science. My view of modern science, of course, is crucial to my argument. The adjective 'modern' is essential. If I am asked what is the difference between the experience produced by seeing a star or by being confronted with a human being, I would say that in the time of Aristotle the difference was negligible. Aristotle's examining the constitution of the Greek states involved the acceptance of no posits different from those of an unscholarly man. Today, the so-called facts of astronomy are not the result of men's having looked at the stars, but of having manipulated instruments and recorded certain sensory experiences arising during the manipulations. Astronomy before the fifteenth century was not a science as I have defined the word. The social sciences are not yet sciences; no *widely accepted* conceptual scheme with posits other than those of common sense has as yet developed. Perhaps someday it will. So I have been assured by friends in economics, sociology, anthropology and psychology, for half a century. I am beginning to doubt it. The failure, I have come to think, is to be traced to the fact that the instruments used in the natural sciences cannot talk back. Human beings can and do. On this basis, experimentation with animals, even if performed by investigators who label themselves 'psychologists', is part of a science, namely biology. Psychology, as an examination of human behaviour, like sociology, is in quite another category. I am inclined to think the history of psychology will bear out my rather unusual dissection of a field which for practical reasons many professors have in recent years endeavoured to consider as a closely knit unit.

I should like to close by examining briefly a normative system, deductions from which can guide the action of a scientist when he closes his laboratory door behind him. Where am I to find it? It will be in the realm of human nature or in the realm of religious experiences, if anywhere at all. I add the qualifying sentence because the question has been raised whether any ethical sentences can have significance.

In the first decades of this century some writers of what is often called the school of linguistic philosophers raised doubts as to whether statements in ethics or morals did more than express emotions. A. J. Ayer, one of the first proponents of what has become known as the emotive-imperative theory wrote in 1936: 'Thus, if I say to someone, " you acted wrongly in stealing that money", I am not stating anything more than if I had simply said, "you stole that money". In

35   3-2

adding that this action is wrong, I am not making any further statement about it, I am simply evincing my moral disapproval.'[16] However satisfying such a point of view was to certain philosophers, it was not likely to find much favour with most laymen for whom moral judgments have meaning. Indeed, over the last thirty years the followers of the linguistic school of thought have considerably modified their positions. Yet, R. M. Hare in his book *The Language of Morals* first published in 1952 has written: 'I gave in the preceding chapter reasons for holding that no moral system whose principles were regarded as purely factual could fulfil its function of regulating our conduct. In this chapter I have shown that no moral system which claims to be based on principles which are self-evident can fulfil this function either. These two contentions between them, if they are accepted, dispose of nearly all of what Hume calls "the vulgar systems of morality".'[17] At the beginning of the paragraph from which I have quoted stands the statement, 'The upshot of all this is rather alarming.' To which a lay moralist might readily agree.

Yet if I am to make the comparison I desire, I must choose some one normative system; I pick a rather loosely connected system which owes its origin to the religious experiences in the Judaic–Christian tradition. Indeed for many persons the system is still located in the realm of religious experiences. Its validity rests either on one's religious experiences or on a firm belief in the dogmas of one branch or another of Judaism or Christianity. Which means, in turn, complete confidence in reported religious experiences. I address myself, however, to others. I have in mind those who would place the system in the realm of human nature, and indeed might consider the realm of religious experiences to be empty. Such people accept the norms of moral conduct not because of a religious faith, but in spite of a lack of it. My choice of a normative system may not meet with the approval of moral philosophers. But I venture to think the number of persons who adhere to it is far larger than the naturalistic moralists would have us believe. Professor Walter Kaufmann has remarked that 'the consensus on what is good and evil is far wider than agreement on the reasons the philosophers have adduced for traditional moral judgements'.[18]

The question of the validity of the original statements in the realm of religious experiences is not at issue. What were once deductions from the 'truths' of a theological system now serve as postulates. The entire system must be appraised much as the entire conceptual scheme of the realm of nature is tested every time an experiment is performed. Not that this normative system or any other is subject to experimental test. The realm of human nature of which this normative scheme is a part does not rest on experiences arising from the manipulation of objects but on experiences arising from personal encounters. Only the total normative scheme can be appraised by examining the conduct of the adherents.

The attitude of the adherents is analogous to that of the dedicated scientist who wishes to be part of an enterprise which can be best defined in terms of what it has accomplished. His ambition is to be a constructive member of an international fraternity which believes science should be advanced. In a somewhat similar way, there are many men and women whose ambition is to be a moral person, though the ambition will not usually be publicly proclaimed. Such people would subscribe to a set of interlocking statements any one of which, if taken by itself, would be difficult to justify and accept. Thus, in one regard the moral conduct of a person committed to be a moral man has a common base with the conduct of the same individual when he functions as a committed scientist.

There might appear to be one particularly important difference between the conduct of the scientist as scientist and the man seeking to be moral. Science is a dynamic undertaking. The scientist is engaged in an operation which is aimed at change, though usually he must be content to being party to a small one. The moralist, unless he be a philosopher or religious prophet, has no such aim. Or so I was once prepared to say. But on further consideration of the arguments put forth by R. M. Hare,[19] I am inclined to think the difference may be more of degree than of kind. Speaking of the principles to be taught by parents, he writes, 'What we do, if we are sensible, is to give him (the child) a solid basis of principles, but at the same time ample opportunity of making decisions upon which these principles are based and by which they are modified, improved, adapted to changed circumstances, or even abandoned if they become entirely unsuited to a new environment.' Or as Professor Frankena has put it, 'We must not only teach our principles and the knowledge to apply them, but must also prepare the younger generation for a certain creativeness or originality in solving moral problems.'[20] Thus, to some extent the moralist can be involved in change. But the moral man envisages his primary function not in forwarding change in the accepted set of postulates which guide his actions but in the development of a society in which an ever larger number of people conduct themselves according to principles he has made his own.

My comparison of two sets of guides to conduct is now complete. One set determines the choices made by a scientist as scientist; the other, the decisions made by the same man facing human problems. If I were to venture a summary, I could put it in two lines: I have presented a sceptical unorthodox view about scientific knowledge and a conventional view of moral conduct. Whether there be any merit in such a rather bizarre combination, I must leave to the members of the audience to decide. It only remains for me to thank the trustees of the Arthur Stanley Eddington Lectureship for the opportunity they have provided for me to present certain ideas which have been rumbling in my mind for more than a decade. I wish to express my gratitude particularly to Princeton University for the gracious hospitality with which I have been received.

ACKNOWLEDGEMENTS

Appreciation is extended by the author to the following publishers and owners of copyright material for permission granted to quote from the below-named works. Pages and publication dates appear in the notes, which follow.

Harvard University Press, *From a Logical Point of View*, by Willard V. Quine, copyright 1953, '61 by the President and Fellows of Harvard College; and, *Toward Reunion in Philosophy* by Morton White, copyright 1956 by the President and Fellows of Harvard College.

Yale University Press, *Science and Common Sense* by James B. Conant.

Holt, Rinehart & Winston, Inc., *The Principles of Psychology* by William James.

Columbia University Press, *Modern Science and Modern Man* by James B. Conant.

Oxford University Press, *The Language of Morals* by R. M. Hare.

Paul R. Reynolds, Inc., *Varieties of Religious Experience* by William James.

Professor William Frankena, *Ethics in an Age of Science*.

40

REFERENCES AND NOTES

1 James B. Conant, *On Understanding Science* (New Haven: Yale University Press, 1947), p. 24. See also James B. Conant, *Science and Common Sense*, (New Haven: Yale University Press, 1951), p. 32. 'Experimental science can be thought of as an activity which increases the adequacy of the concepts and conceptual schemes which are related to certain types of perceptions and which lead to certain types of activities; it is one extension of common sense. For common sense in turn may be thought of as a series of concepts and conceptual schemes which have proved highly satisfactory for the practical uses of mankind. Some of those concepts and conceptual schemes were carried over into science with only a little pruning and whittling and for a long time proved useful. As the recent revolutions in physics indicate, however, many errors can be made by failure to examine carefully just how common sense ideas should be defined in terms of what the experimenter plans to do.'

2 *On Understanding Science*, p. 24.

3 James B. Conant, *Modern Science and Modern Man*, (New York: Columbia University Press, 1952), pp. 50–9. 'One objection to the point of view I am advocating in these lectures may be considered briefly...It is to the effect that if a scientific theory is not even an approximation to a map of a portion of the universe, the so-called advance of pure science is nothing but a game; from which it would follow, so the objection runs, that the justification of science is to be found only in the application of science to the practical arts. The answer to those who put forward arguments of this type is to remind them of the work of mathematicians, painters, poets and musical composers. To my mind, the significance of the fabric of scientific theories that have been produced in the last three hundred-and-fifty years is the same as the

significance of the art of the great periods in history, or the significance of the work of the musical composers. For most scientists, I think the justification of their work is to be found in the pure joy of its creativeness; the spirit which moves them is closely akin to the imaginative vision which inspires an artist...A second objection to the skepticism of those of us who regard all scientific theories as formulation of policy is that our view is only a transitory social phenomenon. One must admit that perhaps the children now in elementary school may in middle life feel that a picture of the universe that seems no picture is quite a satisfactory model...the idea of science as an inquiry into the structure of the universe may once again become firmly established in people's minds. My bet as to the future, however, is on the other horse. It seems to me more likely that the average citizen will come to think of science in totally different terms from those employed in explaining science to lay audiences fifty years ago.' (Before relativity, before quantum theory, when light was regarded as an undulation of the luminiferous ether and definitely *not* composed of particles.)

4 J. J. Thomson, *The Corpuscular Theory of Matter* (London: Archibald Constable and Co. Ltd., 1907), p. 1.

5 *Ethics*, by Stephen C. Pepper of the University of California (New York: Appleton-Century-Crofts, Inc., 1960), gives an admirable account of the principal types of ethical theory.

6 William K. Frankena, *Ethics in An Age of Science.* The Association of Princeton Graduate Alumni: Report of the Eighth Conference held at the Graduate College of Princeton 17–18 June 1960.

7 William Van Orman Quine, *From a Logical Point of View* (Cambridge, Mass.: Harvard University Press, 1953), p. 42.

8 *Ibid.* p. 41.   9 *Ibid.* p. 44.

10 William James, *The Principles of Psychology* (New York:

Henry Holt, 1893), II, 640, footnote. I quote the footnote more fully than in my text. It starts as follows:
'The aspiration to be "scientific" is such an idol of the
tribe to the present generation, is so sucked in with his
mother's milk by every one of us, that we find it hard to
conceive of a creature who should not feel it, and harder
still to treat it freely as the altogether peculiar and one-
sided subjective interest which it is. But, as a matter of
fact, few even of the cultivated members of the race
have shared it; it was invented but a generation or two
ago. In the middle ages, it meant only impious magic;
and the way in which it even strikes orientals [James
was writing in the early 1890s] is charmingly shown in
the letter of a Turkish cadi to an English traveller asking
him for statistical information which Sir A. Layard
prints at the end of his "Nineveh and Babylon". The
document is too full of edification not to be given in
full. It runs thus:

"My Illustrious Friend and Joy of My Liver.
The thing you ask of me is both difficult and useless.
Although I have passed all my days in this place, I have
neither counted the houses nor inquired into the number of inhabitants; and as to what one person loads on
his mules and the other stows away in the bottom of his
ship, that is no business of mine. But, above all, as to the
previous history of this city, God only knows the
amount of dirt and confusion that the infidels may have
eaten before the coming of the sword of Islam. It were
unprofitable for us to inquire into it.
O my soul! O my lamb! seek not after things which
concern thee not. Thou camest unto us and we wel-
comed thee: go in peace..."'

11 Thomas S. Kuhn, *The Structure of Scientific Revolutions*
(Chicago: The University of Chicago Press, 1962).

12 Quine, *From a Logical Point of View*, p. 16.

13 Morton White, *Toward Reunion in Philosophy* (Cambridge, Mass.: Harvard University Press, 1956), p. 255-6.

14 William James, *Varieties of Religious Experience*. The Gifford Lectures on Natural Religion delivered at Edinburgh in 1901–2. (New York: Mentor Edition, 1958), with a foreword by Jacques Barzun.

Since some readers may not be familiar with James's treatment of religious experiences, a few extracts may be in order. In his foreword to the Mentor text, Jacques Barzun says that the word 'varieties' in the title defines James's philosophic temper. James, after pointing out that he is neither a theologian, nor a scholar learned in the history of religion nor an anthropologist, states that as a psychologist he is interested in what he calls 'the religious propensities of man' and proposes to survey them. To this end he presents in twenty long chapters a vast amount of documentary material, which today might be called case histories. His inquiry, he writes, is not religious institutions and their origin. 'The documents that will most concern us', he writes (p. 22), 'will be those of the men who were most accomplished in the religious life and best able to give an intelligible account of their ideas and motives. These men, of course, are either comparatively modern writers or else such earlier ones as have become religious classics ...I may take my citations, my sentences and paragraphs of personal confession, from books that most of you at some time will have had already in your hands, and yet this will be no detriment to the value of my conclusions. ...The question: What are the religious propensities? and the question: What is their philosophic significance? are two entirely different orders of questions from a logical point of view; and, as a failure to recognize this fact distinctly may breed confusion, I wish to insist upon the point a little before we enter into the documents and materials to which I have referred. In recent books on logic, distinction is made between two orders of inquiry concerning anything. First, what is the nature of it? how did it come about? what is its consti-

44

tution, origin, and history? And second, what is its importance, meaning or significance now that it is once here? The answer to the one question is given in an *existential judgement* or proposition. The answer to the other is a *proposition of value*, what the Germans call a *Werthurtheil*, or what we may, if we like, denominate a *spiritual judgement.*'

Though James insists he is concerned with the purely existential point of view, he is at some pains in the early pages to disavow any intention to degrade 'so sublime a subject' as religious experiences, or 'discredit the religious side of life'. However, to many readers at the turn of this century, his readiness to consider religious experiences outside of the framework of a creed may have made him appear as an enemy of true religion (i.e. their own creed). Indeed, in his search for the meaning of his adjective 'religious', he takes himself very far in the direction of 'free thinkers'. Thus, he writes (p. 42): 'Religion, therefore, as I now ask you arbitrarily to take it, shall name for us the *feelings, acts, and experiences of individual men in their solitude, so far as they apprehend themselves to stand in relation to whatever they may consider the divine*...We escape much controversial matter by this arbitrary definition of our field. But, still, a chance of controversy comes up over the word "divine", if we take it in too narrow a sense. There are systems of thought which the world usually calls religious, and yet which do not positively assume a God. Buddhism is in this case. Popularly, of course, the Buddha himself stands in place of God; but in strictness the Buddhistic system is atheistic. Modern transcendental idealism, Emersonianism, for instance, also seems to let God evaporate into abstract Ideality.' Then, after a long quotation from Emerson with comments, James continues as follows: 'The sort of appeal that Emersonian optimism, on the one hand, and Buddhistic pessimism, on the other, make to the individual and the sort of response

45

which he makes to them in his life are in fact indistinguishable from, and in many respects, identical with the best Christian appeal and response. We must, therefore, from the experiential point of view, call those godless or quasi-godless creeds "religions": and, accordingly when in our definition of religion we speak of the individual's relation to "what he considers the divine", we must interpret the term "divine "very broadly, as denoting any object that is god*like*, whether it be a concrete deity or not.'

Some pages later James seeks to withdraw from some of the implications of his broad definition of the word 'divine'. On p. 47 he writes: 'For common men, "religion", whatever more special meanings it may have, signifies always a *serious* state of mind...But, if hostile to light irony, religion is equally hostile to heavy grumbling and complaint...So, I propose—arbitrarily again, if you please—to narrow our definition once more by saying the word "divine" as employed therein, shall mean for us not merely the primal and enveloping and real, for that meaning if taken without restriction might well prove too broad. The divine shall mean for us only such a primal reality as the individual feels impelled to respond to solemnly and gravely, and neither by a curse nor a jest.'

I can do no better than take these sentences as defining what I mean by 'religious' when I write of the 'realm of religiouse xperiences'. I point out again that as far as the experiences in question affect a person's behaviour, they may be either directly responsive as in all James's variety of cases, or a conviction that the recorded experiences of others might well have been one's own or may be in the future. Those who are nominal members only of a sect, do not share in religious experiences as I am using the term.

15 *Modern Science and Modern Man*, pp. 98–9.

The relevant passage in its entirety is as follows:

'As to the unifying materialistic World Hypothesis, my doubt stems from its manifest inadequacy. As a conceptual scheme attempting to account for everything in the whole universe, it seems to me unsatisfactory because it is incomplete. It fails to provide for the altruistic and idealistic side of human nature. It fails to accommodate what I regard as highly significant facts, not facts of science, but facts of human history. These are the unselfish ways in which human beings often act with compassion, love, friendliness, self-sacrifice, the desire to mitigate human suffering. In short, it is the problem of "good", not "evil", that requires some other formulation of human personality than that provided by the usual naturalistic moralist. On the other hand, the formulations that attempt to include spiritual values, modern physics, biology and cosmology within one total consistent scheme attempt, to my mind, far too much. Whether the unifying principle can be a dualism of matter and spirit, mechanism, formism or some form of idealism, the whole attempt seems to me to be in the wrong direction. My preference would be for more adequate exploration of special limited areas of experience; one of these would include those experiences which can be ordered in terms of a system of spiritual values. Each of these restricted areas exploration I venture to designate a universe of inquiry.'

My ideas have changed somewhat since I wrote the above in 1952. For one thing, I have dropped the use of the term 'spiritual values' because it is far too vague. For another, my acceptance of Quine's epistemology as a basis for my original definition of science has moved the focus of my attention to the 'raw experiences' which are being ordered. Therefore, in place of designating the restricted areas of exploration, 'universes of inquiry', I have now suggested we divide raw experience into three realms. I might point out that just as a normative scheme may be located either in the realm of human

47

nature or the realm of religious experience, so many activities which can be said to have 'spiritual value' may be located in either of the two realms or both. Finally, I must admit that my strong inclination to a meaningful interpretation of Job's lament and God's answer out of the whirlwind (pp. 88–90) is open to the following rather caustic comment of William James: 'The constitutionally sombre religious person makes even of his religious peace a very sober thing. Danger still hovers in the air about it...Lie low, for you are in the hands of a living God. In the Book of Job, for example, the impotence of man and the omnipotence of God is the exclusive burden of its author's mind. "It is as high as heaven; what canst thou do?—deeper than hell; what canst thou know? There is an astringent relish about the truth of this conviction which some men can feel, and which for them is as near an approach as can be made to the feeling of religious joy' (*Varieties of Religious Experience*, p. 74).

16 Quoted by P. W. Taylor in his *The Moral Judgment* (Englewood Cliff, New Jersey: Prentice Hall, 1963), p. 120, in the chapter headed 'Ethical Terms and Emotive Expressions'.

17 R. M. Hare *The Language of Morals* (London: Oxford University Press, 1952). Published as a Galaxy Book (New York, 1964), to which the page reference refers, p. 44. For a critique of A. J. Ayer's views and R. M. Hare's, *Ethics* by Stephen C. Pepper cited above (note 5) is most illuminating. See particularly pp. 296–310.

18 Walter Kaufmann, 'Educational Development from the Point of View of Normative Philosophy', *Harvard Educational Review*, XXXVI, no. 3 (1966) p. 254.

19 Hare, *The Language of Morals*, cited above (note 17), pp. 76–7.

20 William K. Frankena, 'Towards a Philosophy of Moral Education', *Harvard Educational Review*, XXVIII, no. 4 (1958), p. 306.